YOU CAN'T WIN,
CHARLIE BROWN

Books by Charles M. Schulz

DEAR GREAT PUMPKIN,

YOU CAN'T WIN, CHARLIE BROWN

A NEW PEANUTS® BOOK

by Charles M. Schulz

HOLT, RINEHART AND WINSTON
New York

First Edition

Library of Congress Catalog Card Number: 62-15623

87752-1212

Printed in the United States of America

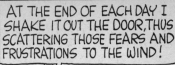

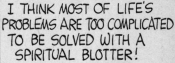

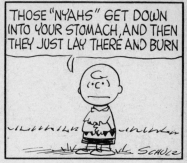

WHEN YOU'RE ON YOUR WAY TO SCHOOL, AND YOU MEET A DOG, YOU SHOULD ALWAYS STOP, AND PAT HIM ON THE HEAD...

PAT PAT

THAT ALWAYS GETS YOUR DAY OFF TO A GOOD START..

SCHULZ

WELL, AT LEAST I'M CONTRIBUTING **SOMETHING** TO SOCIETY!

I'VE JUST BEEN READING ABOUT THE DECLINE AND FALL OF THE ROMAN EMPIRE...

I'VE ALSO READ ABOUT THE DECLINE OF HOLLYWOOD, THE DECLINE OF POPULAR MUSIC, THE DECLINE OF FAMILY LIFE...

THE DECLINE OF IMPERIALISM, THE DECLINE OF MORALITY AND THE DECLINE OF BOXING...

I'VE ALWAYS BEEN FASCINATED BY FAILURE!

SCHULZ

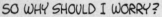

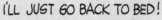

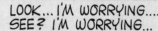

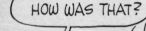

GOOD GRIEF! HERE COMES LUCY! I'M TRAPPED!

SHE SAID SHE'D THROW MY BLANKET IN THE TRASH BURNER THE NEXT TIME SHE SAW IT...

SCHULZ

DO YOU THINK I'M BEAUTIFUL, CHARLIE BROWN?

YOU DIDN'T ANSWER RIGHT AWAY! YOU HAD TO THINK ABOUT IT, DIDN'T YOU?

IF YOU HAD REALLY THOUGHT I WAS BEAUTIFUL, YOU WOULD HAVE SPOKEN RIGHT UP!!

I KNOW WHEN I'VE BEEN INSULTED!! I KNOW WHEN...

GOOD GRIEF!

SCHULZ

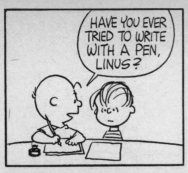

WHAT A SITUATION..

MISS OTHMAR IS GOING TO PROVE TO LINUS THAT YOU CAN BREAK A HABIT WITH SHEER WILL POWER SO SHE'S GOING TO STOP BITING HER FINGERNAILS

LINUS IS SO SURE THAT SHE CAN'T DO IT HE'S RISKING HIS BELOVED BLANKET..

IN THESE TEACHER-PUPIL STRUGGLES IT'S ALWAYS THE PRINCIPAL WHO LOSES!

SCHULZ

HA HA HA! BOY, NOW YOU'VE DONE IT!

YOU MADE AN AGREEMENT WITH YOUR TEACHER TO GIVE UP YOUR BLANKET IF SHE'D GIVE UP CHEWING HER FINGERNAILS...

AND SHE'S DOING IT! AND NOW YOU'RE STUCK!

I FAILED TO RECKON WITH THE TENACITY OF THE MODERN-DAY SCHOOL TEACHER!

SCHULZ

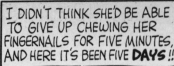

NOW LOOK WHAT YOU'VE DONE... YOU'VE BURIED YOUR LEADER!

I'M THE MOST USELESS PERSON EVER BORN

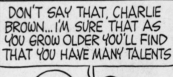

DON'T SAY THAT, CHARLIE BROWN... I'M SURE THAT AS YOU GROW OLDER YOU'LL FIND THAT YOU HAVE MANY TALENTS

HA HA HA HA HA HA HA

I **KNEW** I'D NEVER BE ABLE TO SAY THAT AND KEEP A STRAIGHT FACE!

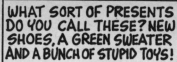

SCHROEDER, YOUR ACTIONS ARE BEYOND MY COMPREHENSION!

HOW CAN YOU GIVE UP BASEBALL JUST TO PLAY THE PIANO?! HOW CAN YOU **DO** THIS?

DON'T YOU REALIZE YOU'RE LETTING DOWN YOUR COUNTRY?

HOW WILL WE WIN THE RACE WITH COMMUNISM IF WE NEGLECT THE THINGS THAT COUNT?

AS LONG AS SCHROEDER HAS QUIT THE TEAM, THE REST OF US ARE GOING TO QUIT, TOO!

IF HE CAN QUIT BECAUSE HE LIKES BEETHOVEN BETTER THAN BASEBALL, WE FEEL THAT WE HAVE A RIGHT TO QUIT, TOO!

GOOD GRIEF!

BEANED BY BEETHOVEN!

HA HA HA LOOK AT THIS IN TODAY'S PAPER...

SOME BLOCKHEAD HAS RUN AN AD IN THE "SITUATIONS WANTED" COLUMN TO GET A JOB AS MANAGER OF A BALL CLUB!

HA HA HA HA HA

WELL, I GUESS IT TAKES ALL KINDS TO MAKE A WORLD...

SOME KINDS WE COULD DO WITHOUT!

ANY RESPONSES TO OUR AD YET, CHARLIE BROWN?

NO, I HAVEN'T HEARD A THING...

WELL, IT'S A LITTLE EARLY YET... I'M SURE SOMEBODY WILL OFFER YOU A JOB AS MANAGER, THOUGH..

I MEAN, THERE **MUST** BE A TEAM **SOMEPLACE** THAT IS **SO** DEEP IN LAST PLACE, AND IS **SO** PANIC STRICKEN THAT IT'S WILLING TO TRY **ANYTHING!**

I DIDN'T PUT THAT VERY WELL, DID I?

NO, YOU DIDN'T!

DEAR SNICKER SNACK CEREAL COMPANY,

I APPRECIATE YOUR OFFER OF ONE HUNDRED REVOLUTIONARY WAR SOLDIERS FOR FIFTEEN CENTS.

HOWEVER, BEING AGAINST VIOLENCE, I AM NOT SURE I WANT THEM.

INSTEAD, COULD I PLEASE HAVE A SET OF PEACE-TIME CIVILIANS?

SCHULZ

YOU'RE NOT RELAXED!

SCHULZ

EACH YEAR THE "GREAT PUMPKIN" RISES OUT OF THE PUMPKIN PATCH THAT HE THINKS IS THE MOST SINCERE

HE'S GOT TO PICK THIS ONE! HE'S **GOT** TO! I DON'T SEE HOW A PUMPKIN PATCH CAN BE MORE SINCERE THAN THIS ONE!

YOU CAN LOOK ALL AROUND AND THERE'S NOT A SIGN OF HYPOCRISY...

NOTHING BUT SINCERITY AS FAR AS THE EYE CAN SEE!

ISN'T LINUS GOING OUT FOR "TRICKS OR TREATS"?

NO, HE'S SITTING IN THE PUMPKIN PATCH WAITING FOR THE GREAT PUMPKIN TO APPEAR

WELL, WHEN YOU GO UP TO THIS NEXT HOUSE, ASK THE LADY FOR AN EXTRA TREAT FOR YOUR LITTLE BROTHER WHO IS SITTING OUT IN THE PUMPKIN PATCH

ALL I GOT FROM HER WAS A VERY PECULIAR LOOK!

IT WAS NICE OF THEM TO ASK ME, BUT I JUST HAD TO SAY, "NO"

I SUPPOSE BECAUSE THEY USE MY PLACE FOR THEIR MEETINGS THEY FELT OBLIGATED TO ASK ME TO JOIN THEIR GROUP

SCHULZ

THEIR MEETINGS ARE BECOMING MORE AND MORE FREQUENT..

THEY USUALLY DON'T LAST VERY LONG, HOWEVER

THEN AGAIN THEY SOMETIMES DON'T BREAK UP 'TIL MIDNIGHT!

SCHULZ

DEAR SANTA CLAUS, ENCLOSED PLEASE FIND LIST OF THINGS I WANT FOR CHRISTMAS.

ALSO, PLEASE NOTE INDICATION OF SIZE, COLOR AND QUANTITY FOR EACH ITEM LISTED.

HOW EFFICIENT CAN YOU GET?

DEAR SANTA, I AM LOOKING FORWARD TO YOUR ARRIVAL.

BRING ME LOTS OF EVERYTHING. THE MORE THE BETTER. REGARDS, LUCY

'TIS THE SEASON TO BE GREEDY

ONE LAST FLING!

PSYCHIATRIC HELP 5¢

WHAT CAN YOU DO WHEN THE PATIENT DOESN'T SAY ANYTHING?

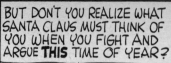

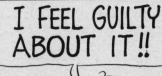

MY HOME IS ALWAYS OPEN TO THOSE WHO ENJOY DISCUSSION GROUPS!

SOONER OR LATER YOU GET TIRED OF HAVING SO MUCH COMPANY!

ONLY **5** MORE SHOPPING DAYS 'TIL BEETHOVEN'S BIRTHDAY

STORES OPEN UNTIL NINE O'CLOCK

WHAT ARE YOU HANGING AROUND HERE FOR? IT'S NOT SUPPERTIME YET!

⁂ SIGH ⁂

MY STOMACH-CLOCK MUST BE FAST..

MMMM

OH, CUT IT OUT!

NOT KNOWING HOW TO PURR IS A GREAT HANDICAP!

SCHULZ

SPACE IS TOO LARGE..

WE DON'T REALLY NEED ALL THAT ROOM..MOST OF THOSE PLANETS AND STARS ARE WAY TOO BIG!

THE WHOLE SOLAR SYSTEM NEEDS READJUSTING...

WHAT CAN WE, AS INDIVIDUALS, DO?

SCHULZ

ALL RIGHT, SO I'M A BASEBALL SCOUT...WHAT DO I DO?

YOU GO, AND FIND OUT ALL YOU CAN ABOUT THEIR PITCHERS AND HITTERS..

WRITE EVERYTHING YOU FIND OUT ON THIS SQUARE OF BUBBLE GUM..IF THEY SUSPECT THAT YOU'RE SCOUTING THEM, YOU CAN JUST CHEW UP THE EVIDENCE...

WELL, GOOD LUCK, OL' BUDDY...

THANK YOU, CHARLIE BROWN..

SOMEHOW I HAVE THE FEELING OF IMPENDING DOOM!

MAYBE I SHOULDN'T HAVE SENT LINUS OUT AS A BASEBALL SCOUT...

MAYBE HE'LL GET LOST..MAYBE THE OTHER TEAM WILL SEE WHAT HE'S DOING, AND BEAT HIM UP...

HEY, MANAGER, DO YOU THINK MY HAIR LOOKS ALL RIGHT THIS WAY, OR SHOULD I CHANGE IT?

NO, IT LOOKS FINE JUST THE WAY IT IS...

IT'S AWFUL TO HAVE TO BE THE ONE WHO MAKES ALL THE DECISIONS!

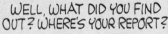

THE WORST THING ABOUT GLASSES IS TRYING TO KEEP THEM CLEAN!

FOR SOME REASON THAT'S WORSE THAN EVER!

THEY DIDN'T TASTE VERY GOOD EITHER!

SCHULZ

NOT AGAIN?

YES, AND I CAN'T FIND THEM ANYWHERE!

WELL, IF YOU'RE GOING TO WEAR GLASSES, YOU'RE GOING TO HAVE TO LEARN TO HANG ON TO THEM!

"GENTLEMEN, I'D LIKE TO PRESENT TO YOU THE NEW CHAIRMAN OF THE BOARD!"

SCHULZ

OH, THIS IS AN IDEAL RABBIT-CHASING DAY!

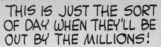

THIS IS JUST THE SORT OF DAY WHEN THEY'LL BE OUT BY THE MILLIONS!

C'MON, SNOOPY, LET'S GET OUT AND SNIFF THOSE RABBITS!

YOU DON'T SNIFF RABBITS, YOU **SEE** THEM!

SCHULZ

ALL RIGHT! LET'S HAVE THOSE GLASSES!

GOOD GRIEF! IF IT ISN'T ONE THING, IT'S ANOTHER!

HE WAS JUST JEALOUS BECAUSE I LOOKED SO DISTINGUISHED!

SCHULZ

ZOOM

WITH A LITTLE PRACTICE I BET I COULD GET THE SHOES, TOO!

SCHULZ

BOY, THESE GLASSES SURE GET DIRTY!

I'VE SEEN FACTORY WINDOWS THAT WERE CLEANER THAN THIS!

I HAVE JUST THE THING FOR YOU, LINUS... I'VE CUT UP A WHOLE BUNCH OF LITTLE FLANNEL SQUARES FOR YOU TO USE TO WIPE YOUR GLASSES!

WELL, NOW, WASN'T THAT THOUGHTFUL OF HER? NICE LITTLE FLANNEL SQUARES... JUST THE SORT THAT ONE MIGHT GET IF ONE CUT UP ONE'S...........

......**BLANKET!**

SCHULZ

WHAT COLOR IS A PEACE CONFERENCE?

OF COURSE, I REALIZE THAT THERE WILL ALWAYS BE CRITICISM..

ALL MEDIUMS OF ENTERTAINMENT GO THROUGH THIS..EVEN OUR HIGHER ART FORMS HAVE THEIR DETRACTORS...THE THEATRE SEEMS ESPECIALLY VULNERABLE..

AND GOODNESS KNOWS HOW MUCH CRITICISM IS LEVELED AT OUR TELEVISION PROGRAMMING..ONE SOMETIMES WONDERS IF IT IS POSSIBLE EVER TO PLEASE THE VAST MAJORITY OF PEOPLE...

THE MOST RECENT CRITICISM IS THAT THERE IS TOO LITTLE ACTION AND FAR TOO MUCH TALKING IN THE MODERN-DAY COMIC STRIP... WHAT DO YOU THINK ABOUT THIS?

RIDICULOUS!